ANNE MCCAFFREY was born on April 1st, an auspicious natal day, and has lived life to the full ever since. She graduated *cum laude* from Radcliffe College where she majored in Slavonic languages and literature. After appearing as a witch in the American premiere of Carl Orff's opera *Ludus de Nato Infante Mirificus*, for which production she was also stage manager, Anne McCaffrey divided her time between three small children and writing short stories. By the time the children were comfortably in school, she had achieved enough literary success to devote herself full time to writing. Her first novel, *Restoree*, was written in protest against the unrealistic portrayal of women in the science fiction of the 1950s, but her vibrant imagination led her naturally to broader themes and the creation of fictional worlds. The ten novels in the *Dragonriders of Pern* series have linked Anne McCaffrey's name forever with dragons, the great and mythical beasts of air and fire. Her huge success is testament to the depth of emotion she reveals in human relationships with dragons. Anne McCaffrey now lives in County Wicklow, Ireland, in a house built to her own design and named 'Dragonhold-Underhill'. When not busy writing or travelling around the world to lecture in universities and secondary schools, she occasionally rides a black and white mare named Pi to and from the livery stables she has established there.

_____

THE ARTISTS

Lela Ann Dowling

the pencil artist on Dragonflight, lives in Novato,
California. Her art is highly sought after at science
fiction and fantasy conventions. She has adapted *Alice in
Wonderland* for the graphic form, and illustrated the
book *Faerie Tale* by Raymond E. Feist. Her other credits
include work on the video games *The Eidolon*, *Loom* and
Young Indy.

Cynthia Martin

lives in Northern California. She has worked for every
major comic publisher in America, and on several major
series, including *Wonder Woman*, *Adolescent Radioactive
Black Belt Hamsters 3-D*, *War of the Gods* and *Total
Eclipse*.

Fred Von Tobel

lives in New York. His most recent credits include 'The
Madonna' for Clive Barker's *Tapping the Vein* series.

ANNE MCCAFFREY

DRAGONFLIGHT

Adapted by Brynne Stephens

Illustrated by Lela Dowling, Cynthia Martin
and Fred Von Tobel

Eclipse  Books

Eclipse Graphic Novels
An Imprint of Eclipse Books and HarperCollins *Publishers*

Available to the comic book trade in the U.S. and Canada from
Eclipse Books
P.O. Box 1099
Forestville, California 95436

Published by Eclipse Books 1993
9 8 7 6 5 4 3 2 1

Cloth: ISBN 1 56060 175 2
Trade paperback: ISBN 1 56060 176 0

Copyright © Anne McCaffrey 1991
Adaptation Copyright © Brynne Stephens 1991
Artwork Copyright © Lela Dowling, Fred Von Tobel &
Cynthia Martin 1991

Printed and bound in Hong Kong

MYTH IS AN UNPREDICTABLE THING. AND MEN TOOK THEIR PROPENSITY FOR IT TO THE STARS WITH THEM, FOR NOTHING ENGENDERS DISBELIEF LIKE DISTANCE -- IN SPACE OR TIME...

HUMANS COLONIZED A PLANET, FORGETTING EARTH AS THEY RELAXED INTO THEIR OWN NEW HISTORY, THEIR OWN MYTHS. MYTHS BASED ON NEW DANGERS, FOUGHT AND WON... AND THEN FORGOTTEN.

BUT THE UNIVERSE OFTEN
FINDS WAYS TO REMIND ITS
CHILDREN THAT **SAFETY** IS AS
MUCH A MYTH AS ANY OTHER...

ASLEEP IN HER OWN FORGETTING, ONCE AGAIN LESSA AWAKES COLD.

A NIGHTMARE, AGAIN. BUT NOT THE FIRE AND BLOOD, THE SCREAMS...

...THIS TIME, SOMETHING WORSE.

THERE ARE STORIES ABOUT THAT STAR, WARNINGS OF DANGER... BUT OF WHAT KIND?

NO MATTER WHAT HAPPENS, LOVE, YOU DON'T KNOW ME.

< NO NO WON'T CAN'T LOVE FRIEND MISTRESS LOVE LOVE --›

DAWN... AND THE LIGHT'S HURTING YOU, POOR THING. I MUST GO IN: PROMISE!

< PROMISE DON'T WANT TO SAD SAD SAD PROMISE SAD ›

IF SOMETHING BAD'S COMING TO RUATHA...

...I SHALL GIVE IT THE HELP IT NEEDS!

AND NOW THE CRAFTHOLDS? HOW WILL WE FIND A CANDIDATE WITH ALL OF THE WOMEN HIDING-- BEING HIDDEN?

NO MATTER-- IT'S NOT WOMEN I'M AFTER JUST NOW.

WHAT IF WE DON'T FIND ANYONE? I ALMOST WISH JORA HADN'T DIED.

JORA WAS A DISASTER. SHE HAD NO CONTROL, AND SO THE WEYR SUFFERS WITH SMALL CLUTCHES AND FEW DRAGONS.

TRUE. WE NEED MORE DRAGONS. WHEN THREAD COMES--

THERE'S BEEN NO THREAD FOR TWO HUNDRED TURNS. THE HOLDERS SAY THERE'LL BE NO MORE.

L'TOL?

IT'S "LYTOL", NOW. AND YOU, F'LAR AND F'NOR, BOTH FAVOR YOUR SIRE. COME IN AND WE'LL TALK.

THAT'S L'TOL?

THE BROWN RIDER FROM S'LEL'S WING, YES.

"HE LOST HIS DRAGON IN THE SPRING GAMES. AN ACCIDENT WITH ANOTHER BEAST'S DRAGONFIRE."

FIVE HOLDS LATER, FROM THE COLD OF *BETWEEN*--

--TO A VALLEY FROZEN IN HATRED.

< LOOK AT THIS PLACE! NO WONDER FAX INSISTED WE SEARCH HERE LAST!>

< I THINK FAX LIKES TO INSIST...>

<THAT MIGHT'VE WORKED ON R'GUL, BUT NOT ON ME.>

< I THINK YOU ALSO LIKE TO INSIST...>

< I MUST, TO REMIND THE HOLDER LORDS OF THEIR DUTIES.>

<STRANGE...>

< AND STUPID! THE OLD WAYS--->

< NO--SOMETHING *HERE* IS STRANGE. SOME POWER. STRONG, BUT--STRANGE.>

< CIRCLE AROUND AGAIN. AND ALERT THE OTHER DRAGONS.>

A DREAM SO DARK, SO COLD, THAT EVEN THE SUN CANNOT WARM HER. SHE WISHES FOR A DISTRACTION--

--AND GETS ONE.

DRAGONS...

THE DREAM OF DANGER TURNS TO ONE OF REVENGE.

...TRASH ON THE FLOOR, BLOCKED CHIMNEYS; IT'S AWFUL!

AND IT SMELLED LIKE *ANIMALS* HAD BEEN IN THERE!

EXCUSE ME...

POOR LADY GEMMA, AT HER *AGE*...

THIS WAS SUCH A GRACEFUL HALL, IT WAS A NOBLE LINE.

LADY GEMMA, MIGHT ONE OF THE BLOOD HAVE-- ESCAPED?

PLEASE -- BE CAREFUL, LORD F'LAR!

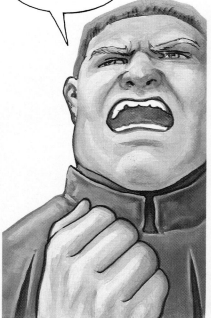
HOW LONG AM I SUPPOSED TO WAIT FOR FOOD IN MY OWN HOLD?!

THIS IS WHAT YOU OFFER YOUR LORD?

I'M SORRY, MY LORD, IF I'D HAD NOTICE I WOULD HAVE SENT TO CROM FOR EXTRA FOOD--

SENT TO CROM?! THE DAY ONE OF MY HOLDS CANNOT SUPPORT A VISIT BY ITS LORD, I'LL RENOUNCE IT...

RROOOOOAAAAARRR!!

< YES, I FEEL IT, MNEMENTH! THE POWER! >

WHAT'S WRONG WITH YOUR BEASTS, DRAGONMAN?

OH, THEY OFTEN ROAR. AT SUNSET, FLOCKS OF WHERRIES, MEALTIMES...

ROOAAR!

YOU MEAN... THEY'RE HUNGRY?

NO, THEY WERE JUST FED. FIVE DAYS AGO.

HAHAHAHA! I'LL RENOUNCE IT IN FAVOR OF HER BABE -- IF IT'S MALE, AND *IF* IT LIVES!

HEARD AND WITNESSED!

HEARD AND WITNESSED!

GET THE BIRTHING-WOMAN!

WHAT MADE YOU SAY THAT?

I DON'T KNOW, BUT *SOMETHING* DID. THAT POWER -- IT'S DEFINITELY FEMALE. BUT WHO?

IT'S THAT *GIRL!* FAX'S BLOW STOPPED THE POWER!

AND IF I DON'T KILL FAX--

HE'LL KILL *HER* --

AND ALL OF PERN WILL BE LOST.

< WERE YOU LOOKING FOR THIS? >

YIYIYIYIYI!!!

YOU'RE NOT THE LIAR YOU THINK. THE BABE LIVES, CUT FROM ITS MOTHER'S WOMB-- AND IT'S MALE.

RUATHA IS MINE.

YOU HAVE MORE IMPORTANT THINGS TO DO. WE SEARCH FOR A NEW WEYRWOMAN.

WEYRWOMAN??

SHE'S AFRAID!

RUATHA'S BLOOD HAS THINNED...

NO! I JUST... NEVER THOUGHT BEYOND FAX'S DEATH.

AAAOOOOO!

ROOOAAARRRRR!!

NO! DON'T KILL!

AIIIIII--

CRRAAACK!

IT THOUGHT TO DEFEND ME.

AAARRROOOOOOOOOO!

THEY'RE KEENING FOR HIM--PAYING HIM TRIBUTE!

BUT HE WAS JUST A WATCHWHER...

THE DRAGONS CONFER HONOR WHERE THEY WILL.

THIS ENTRANCE LEADS ONLY TO OUR QUARTERS.

"OUR" QUARTERS?

I NEED TO FEED MNEMENTH. YOU GO BATHE IN THERE. HERE--

TO BE CLEAN AGAIN, WITH NO REASON TO HIDE...

< SHE DOESN'T TRUST YOU A BIT. BUT SHE'S NOT AFRAID OF *ME*! >

< WHY SHOULD SHE BE AFRAID OF YOU? YOU'RE COUSIN TO HER BEST FRIEND THE WATCHWHER...>

< NO SCRAWNY, GROUNDBOUND WATCHWHER IS ANY COUSIN OF *MINE*. >

< BUT YOU GAVE HIM DRAGON TRIBUTE WHEN HE DIED. >

< HE WAS HONORABLE! >

LET THEM BRING HUNDREDS. ALL WE NEED IS *ONE*.

THE WING'S RETURNED--THERE WAS DANCING WHEN PEOPLE HEARD FAX WAS DEAD. LYTOL WILL MAKE A FINE WARDER FOR THE BABE.

AND THE OTHER SEARCHES?

SEVEN OTHERS, PRETTY AND STRONGWILLED.

THERE IS NO END TO THE STREAM OF HOT WATER --

AND YET IT CAN'T WARM HER.

SO I AM TO BE WEYRWOMAN-- BUT HOW?

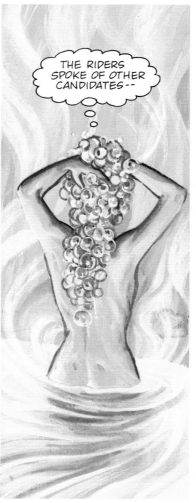

THE RIDERS SPOKE OF OTHER CANDIDATES--

SO HOW WILL ONE BE CHOSEN?

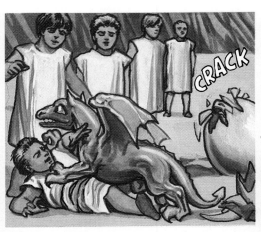

THE WORLD TURNS AND TIMES CHANGE.
OLD DANGERS FADE OUT OF MIND —

— BUT NOT OUT OF TIME.

IT HAS BEEN TWO TURNS SINCE LESSA IMPRESSED GOLDEN RAMOTH AND BECAME WEYRWOMAN.

...AGAIN : STAR SHONE WATCH SCAN SKY. READY THE WEYRS, ALL RIDERS FLY —

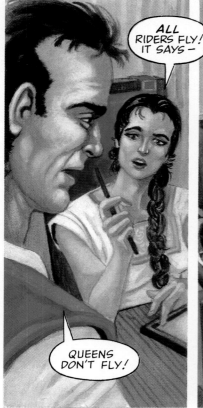

ALL RIDERS FLY! IT SAYS —

QUEENS DON'T FLY!

THEN WHY DO THEY HAVE WINGS ?

THEY FLY TO MATE !

AND ONLY TO MATE! IT'S TRADITION !

I NEED TIME TO THINK.

AND I THINK IT'S TIME TUENTH AWAKENED.

< OH, TUENTH... >

¿ URMPH ?

TUENTH IS AWAKE!

AND MANORA IS HERE!

LESSONS ARE DONE FOR TODAY, THEN.

MNEMENTH SAYS SHE'LL GET BETTER.

SPLOOOSH!

"THE TIME BETWEEN THREADFALLS. IT'S BEEN FOUR HUNDRED YEARS."

"ENOUGH TIME FOR THE HOLDERS TO FORGET WHY THEY NEED US."

IF THEY GET MAD ENOUGH AT K'NET'S RAIDING, THEY'LL ALSO FORGET THEIR FEAR OF US!

I DIDN'T KNOW F'LAR WAS RAIDING AS WELL!

NO ONE TELLS ME ANYTHING!

HATH IS BLOODING HIS KILL-BINTH AND ORTH, TOO!

BLOODING-?

RAMOTH RISES TO MATE! CALL F'LAR!

NO ONE CAN FIND HIM-AND HE'S NOT THE ONLY BRONZE.

I'LL TAKE RAMOTH BETWEEN BEFORE HATH FLIES HER!

YOU DON'T GET TO CHOOSE! TOO BAD NO ONE CAN FIND F'LAR...

...BUT SOME THINGS ARE TIMELESS.

THE WORLD TURNS...AND DAWN COMES.

IT'S COMING SOON.

MNEMENTH...DID F'NOR—

<YES—CANTH SAYS THE RED STAR WAS AT THE TOP OF THE EYE ROCK.>

<TOO MANY MYSTERIES... WHO CALLED US BACK?>

<TROUBLE- HOLDER LORDS IN FORCE ON THE LAKE PLATEAU.>

THERE'S TROUBLE.

LORD HOLDERS, IN FORCE.

YES. YOU SHOULDN'T HAVE SENT K'NET!

<WATCH YOUR STEP WITH HER, F'LAR.>

THE TUNNEL IS THE ONLY WAY INTO THE WEYR?

THAT AND DRAGONBACK, THOUGH I'VE SENT A PARTY TO SCOUT THE CLIFFS.

AND IF THEY SEE THE SCOUTS?

THEY KNOW WE'RE HERE. LOOK.

I SPEAK FOR THE HOLDERS. THE WEYR IS OBSOLETE.

WE WILL NO LONGER TITHE, NOR PERMIT SEARCHES.

YOU *WILL* TITHE - WITHIN THREE DAYS.

AND IF WE DON'T?

WE'LL KEEP YOUR LADIES. BUT THEY'LL BE TREATED LIKE HONORED GUESTS — YOU NEEDN'T FEAR FOR THEM.

MY WIFE!

THREE DAYS, THEN.

DRAGONMEN DO NOT ORDER LORD HOLDERS!

BUT WE *DO* PROTECT YOU! LISTEN TO YOUR HARPERS—THE PORTENTS ARE THERE! THREAD *WILL* FALL!

MYTHS! HARPER NONSENSE!

RAMOTH HAS RISEN TO MATE, AND FLOWN LONG...

AND OUR WEYRWOMAN COMES FROM RUATHA, AS DID THE GREATEST WEYRWOMEN IN HISTORY!

‹MNEMENTH, *WHAT* IS SHE DOING?›

‹SHE'S FLYING, F'LAR. BEAUTIFULLY.›

R'GUL AND F'LAR HAD IT OUT AGAIN. F'LAR WON.

WELL, HE WON'T WIN WITH ME!

THE RED STAR APPEARED IN THE EYE ROCK THIS MORNING! I'D'VE LIKED TO SEE IT!

YOU ALREADY BELIEVE. AND YOU NEEDED REST —

— SO YOU CAN FLY *BETWEEN*.

YOU'LL TEACH ME TODAY?

MEET ME AT THE TOP OF THE RIDGE WHEN RAMOTH'S FED.

I HAD THE DREAM AGAIN, F'LAR. THE WARNING, AND THE *COLD*...

YOU'VE REASON ENOUGH FOR NIGHTMARES.

MEMORY LIES. YOU'RE NOT THAT CHILD NOW.

NO, I'M WEYRWOMAN OF BENDEN. AND READY TO FLY.

YES! WHEN FAX INVADED RUATHA... I KNEW.

TO GO *BETWEEN*, YOU NEED A REFERENCE POINT.

THE STAR STONE?

THAT'S OUR FIRST JUMP. MNEMENTH WILL VISUALIZE IT FOR RAMOTH, AND SHE FOR YOU. READY?

YES! LET'S GO!

READY... *JUMP!*

BETWEEN IS DARK AND COLD—OUTSIDE OF LIGHT, OUTSIDE OF TIME.

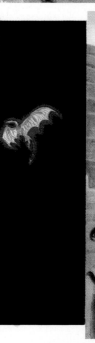

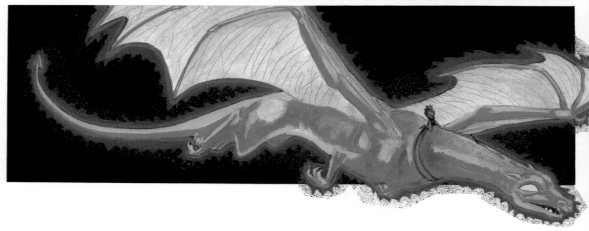

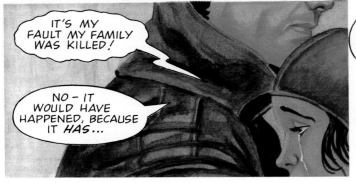

RRROOOAAARRR!

AAOOOO...

THIS ISN'T TOO BAD, F'NOR, BUT IT WILL SCAR.

KYLARA! GO SEE TO THE KITCHENS, THE MEN WILL NEED FOOD.

AND YOU NEED REST, F'LAR.

THERE ISN'T TIME TO REST.

WE NEED TO FIND ANSWERS.

BUT WHERE?

MAYBE THE RECORDS WILL TELL US HOW ONE UNDERSTRENGTH WEYR CAN DO THE FIGHTING OF SIX.

ALL *I* KNOW IS: FIRST, WE NEED MORE DRAGONS. SECOND, WE NEED THEM *NOW*. THIRD, WE NEED GROUND-FIRE--

AND FOURTH, WE NEED SLEEP!

YOU'VE ONE THING ON YOUR MIND, HAVEN'T YOU?

ME? YOU'RE AS SINGLEMINDED AS KYLARA, THAT WAY.

SHALL I OPEN FORT WEYR FOR KYLARA?

I WISH SHE WERE *TURNS* AWAY, AS WELL AS MILES!

THAT'S IT! WE'LL SEND KYLARA AND THE DRAGONETS *BETWEEN* TIMES SO THE YOUNG ONES CAN GROW!

BUT WHERE TO SEND THEM? AND WHEN?

SEND THEM *HERE!*

TO THE SOUTHERN CONTINENT.

BUT THERE'S NO WEYR, NO HATCHING GROUNDS--NOTHING!

WE DON'T KNOW THAT!

TRUE-- SO YOU AND F'NOR WILL GO FIND OUT!

WHILE YOU DEAL WITH THE LORD HOLDERS...

BUT FIRST I HAVE TO DEAL WITH YOU...

F'LAR?

HE'S BEEN GONE AWHILE, BECAUSE THE SCAR HAS HEALED. BUT WE JUST THOUGHT OF THE IDEA THIS MINUTE!

SO HE DID GO, EVEN THOUGH WE KNOW THE PLAN WILL FAIL.

WE DON'T KNOW IT *FAILED* -- BUT WHAT WENT WRONG?

I THINK I KNOW... GOING *BETWEEN* TO RUATHA'S PAST UPSET YOU; YOU THOUGHT YOU CAUSED YOUR FAMILY'S MASSCRE.

BUT MAYBE IT'S SEEING *YOURSELF* THAT CAUSES THE EXTREME SHOCK...

IT'S TOO HARD BEING TWO PLACES AT ONCE... IN TWO *TIMES*!

WE'LL TELL F'NOR OF THE PLAN IN THE MORNING-- BUT SAY NOTHING ABOUT HIS PREMATURE RETURN.

A SINGLE LARGE CLUTCH FROM PRIDITH, OR JUST THE FORTY GROWN DRAGONETS COULD MAKE THE DIFFERENCE.

THAT TAKES CARE OF PROBLEMS ONE AND TWO...

IT'S TIME WE DEALT WITH NUMBER FOUR -- DECISIVELY!

THE FIRST ATTACK WAS MET AND SEARED ABOVE NERAT. WE NEED YOU TO ORGANIZE JUNGLE PATROLS--

BUT-- YOU SAID THE THREAD WAS SEARED IN THE SKY...

THREAD BURROWS-- THERE'S NO SENSE TAKING CHANCES.

THREAD WILL FALL AGAIN IN THREE DAYS AND FOUR HOURS, BEGINNING IN TELGAR AND--

HOW CAN YOU BE SO CERTAIN?

THREAD FALLS IN DEFINITELY PREDICTABLE PATTERNS. THE ATTACKS...

SO YOU SAY! YOU ALSO SAID THEY'D BEGIN FALLING RIGHT AFTER SOLSTICE!

WHICH THEY DID. IN THE NORTHERN HOLDS-- AS BLACK DUST.

THAT DUST IS DANGEROUS?!

IT'S BEEN FALLING FOR WEEKS, HAS IT CAUSED HARM YET?

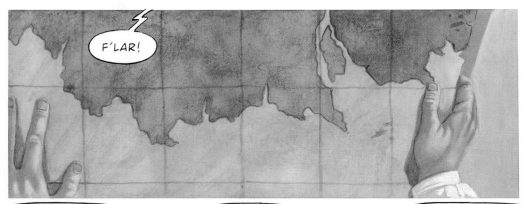

F'LAR!

SUCCESS! BUT HOW YOU KNEW TO SEND EXACTLY THIRTY-TWO CANDIDATES, I'LL NEVER KNOW.

IS THERE A QUEEN EGG?

NO, BUT THERE ARE FOURTEEN BRONZES!

HOW GOES THE WEYR, OTHERWISE?

KYLARA'S A PROBLEM, BUT MAYBE N'TON'S BRONZE WILL FLY PRIDITH NEXT TIME--T'BOR IS SO TOUCHY NO ONE GOES NEAR HIM.

AND YO SUPPLIE

WE EAT THE WAY DRAGONMEN SHOULD--I WISH YOU'D LET ME SEND YOU MORE!

NO, GOING **BETWEEN** TIMES IS TOO HARD. YOU SHOULD GO NOW; YOU'LL BE HERE SOON.

I'LL BE BACK WHEN PRIDITH LAYS THE SECOND CLUTCH!

WAS THAT TANNED YOUNG MAN F'NOR?

YES AND NO... YOU MAKE A GOOD CHAMPION, MASTERHARPER.

YOU HAVE A NOBLE CAUSE, WEYRLEADER.

AND A MORE DESPERATE ONE THAN YOU LET ON, I THINK.

WE HAVE ONLY SEVENTY-TWO NEW DRAGONS, AND THE INTERVALS ARE GETTING SHORTER.

BACK IN TIME... AND YOU CAN JUMP FORWARD, TOO?

WELL, NOT TO A WHEN THAT YOU'VE NEVER SEEN. IT WOULD BE TOO RISKY.

BUT RAMOTH ONLY LAID FORTY. WHERE ARE THEY, BY THE WAY? I EXPECTED THE WEYR TO BE DROWNING IN DRAGONETS.

NOT WHERE, BUT *WHEN*. I SENT THEM *BETWEEN* TIMES TO GROW UP. THE F'NOR YOU SAW CAME FROM THERE. FROM *THEN*.

HERE'S THE CHART TO BE COPIED FOR THE ORD HOLDERS. I CAN ALREADY HEAR THE QUESTIONS...

SPEAKING OF WHICH, THERE'S AN OLD TEACHING SONG YOU SHOULD HEAR. AN UNEASY BALLAD...

C'GAN KEPT HIS GUITAR IN FINE SHAPE...THIS IS CALLED THE QUESTION SONG.

SMELLS RIGHT, LOOKS RIPE, FEELS RIPE...

LET US EAT AND DIE TOGETHER!

A FRUITFUL AND LOVELY PLACE!

BUT SO EXPOSED! NO CLIFFS, OR CAVES...

...RAMOTH, CANTH; COULD YOU LIVE WITHOUT A WEYR?

<WE DID NOT ALWAYS LIVE IN CAVES.>

<I WOULD LIKE IT HERE, BUT I AM NOT TO COME.>

LET'S GO AND TELL F'LAR--HE'S GOING TO BE SO SURPRISED!

SOMEHOW I DOUBT THAT...

WHAT IS HE DOING?

ANTICIPATING SUCCESS.

I STARTED PACKING AND ALERTED THE RIDERS ON THE CHANCE THAT YOU'D SUCCEED. *WE'VE* ONLY GOT THREE DAYS.

BUT I'LL HAVE TEN TURNS.

YOU'LL TAKE THIRTY-TWO CANDIDATES, AND YOUR OWN WING TO TRAIN THEM. YOU HAVE TO START SHIFTING BY EVENING.

SUPPOSE WE'D FOUND THE CONTINENT BARREN?

BUT WE-- YOU'D HAVE GONE TO HIGH REACHES INSTEAD.

CAN YOU DRAW ME SOME REFERENCES, LESSA? WHERE EXACTLY YOU WENT.

NERAT HOLD.

HUNDREDS AND THOUSANDS IN THIS ONE BURROW!

THE STALKS ARE WITHERING AS WE SPEAK! DO SOMETHING!

IS THERE ANYTHING YOU CAN DO, FANDAREL?

I MADE A ROUGH AGENOTHREE SPRAYER. BRING IT HERE!

WHAT WILL THAT DO TO MY CROPS?

NOTHING -- IN DILUTED FORM, IT'S FERTILIZER.

IT WORKED!

BUT IT WOULD TAKE TOO LONG TO DIG UP EVERY BURROW!

BEST TO GET THEM IN THE AIR, BUT THIS CONTRAPTION IS TOO BULKY, TOO HEAVY. I NEED THAT TAPESTRY!

I'LL FIND IT, I PROMISE.

<LESSA IS AWAKE.>

THANK YOU, MASTERSMITH. KEEP WORKING.

LYTOL IS HERE, WITH B'RANT, ON FANTH.

<THANKS, MNEMENTH-- AND DON'T YOU ENCOURAGE THAT STUBBORN WOMAN!>

BRINGING BAD NEWS?

I BRING THE MISSING TAPESTRY.

IT'S BEAUTIFUL! THOSE COLORS!

A LIFETIME'S WORK.

HERE ARE THE DESIGNS FANDAREL NEEDS!

THIS IS THE MAIN DOOR TO RUATH HOLD-- BUT IT ISN'T.

TRUE -- IT'S THE SAME, BUT DIFFERENT.

THIS TAPESTRY BELONGS AT RUATHA. PLEASE ALLOW ME TO ESCORT IT THERE MYSELF, TOMORROW. YOU MUST BE HUNGRY.

THANK YOU, WEYRWOMAN.

I'VE NEVER HEARD THE WEYRWOMAN SOUND SO DOCILE.

RAMOTH'S YOUNG, BUT NOT THAT FOOLISH. SHE CAN'T BE.

BETWEEN IS BLACK AND COLD...
TIMELESS, LIGHTLESS, NOTHING.

IT'S MORNING, AND STILL MNEMENTH CAN'T HEAR THEM. SHE'S GONE.

LESSA WOULDN'T JUMP WITHOUT A REFERENCE POINT!

THE TAPESTRY! SHE SAW *SOMETHING* IN THE TAPESTRY!

WE'VE GOT TO GET TO RUATHA!

YOU'RE CERTAIN SHE TRIED THIS JUMP?

MNEMENTH CAN HEAR AN ECHO FROM CANTH, TEN TURNS AWAY, BUT NOTHING FROM RAMOTH OR LESSA ANYWHERE.

THE DOORWAY-- SHE WAS UNCOMMONLY INTERESTED IN THAT!

THEN SHE *DID* HAVE A REFERENCE! THEY'RE SAFE!

GOING BACK TEN TURNS IS DRAINING F'NOR-- WHO KNOWS WHAT FOUR HUNDRED MIGHT DO?

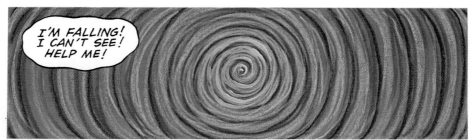

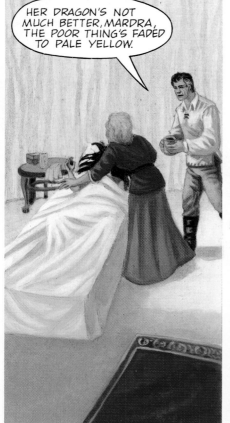

HOW DID YOU FIND US? WHAT WAS YOUR REFERENCE?

THE TAPESTRY--IT SHOWED MEN FIGHTING THREAD, AND PEOPLE ON THE GROUND WITH FLAME-THROWERS--AND THE MAIN DOOR AT RUATH.

MY FATHER JUST COMMISSIONED SUCH A TAPESTRY!

IF SHE KNOWS ABOUT THAT, IT MUST BE TRUE!

WHAT HAPPENED TO ALL THE WEYRS?

THEY--WE WENT WITH YOU, DIDN'T WE? HOW DID YOU KNOW?

THE MASTER-HARPER WROTE A TEACHING SONG, AND I FIGURED IT OUT.

I'LL SEND FOR HIM AT ONCE, AND CALL A COUNCIL OF WEYRLEADERS.

BUT HOW DO WE KNOW THE OTHERS WILL WANT TO COME?

DRAGONFOLK FIGHT THREAD. WHERE--OR WHEN-EVER IT IS.

THEY HAVE TO AGREE--BECAUSE THEY ALREADY HAVE.

BETWEEN IS BLACK AND COLD; AGAIN--

--AND THEN MORE AGAINS...

THIS LAST JUMP WILL TAKE US THROUGH TIME AND PLACE-- TO RUATHA.

YOU ARE A BRAVE WOMAN.

SHE IS A WEYRWOMAN!

BUT I BROUGHT THEM, F'LAR! ALL BUT BENDEN WEYR! THIS IS MARDRA, AND T'TON OF FORT WEYR--

WE BROUGHT EIGHTEEN HUNDRED DRAGONS, AND SEVENTEEN QUEENS, WITH ENOUGH SUPPLIES TO REOPEN OUR WEYR.

AND FLAMETHROWERS-- LESSA SAID YOU NEEDED THEM.

BUT-- TO COME HERE... AL'L OF YOU...

DRAGONMEN MUST FLY, MY FRIEND...

WE WORKED NIGHT AND DAY, BUT THERE ARE ENOUGH FLAMETHROWERS TO GO AROUND.

KYLARA WILL BE SETTLED IN THE SOUTHERN CONTINENT NOW THAT THERE ARE NO EMPTY WEYRS.

ALL THAT'S LEFT NOW IS THREAD.

YOUR CHARTS ARE A WORK OF GENIUS, F'LAR.

THANK YOU, WE'LL NEED LESSA AT TELGAR THIS MORNING -- SHE CAN TALK TO ANY DRAGON.

OF COURSE -- MARDRA DOESN'T MIND.

WHY WOULD SHE?

WELL, AS SENIOR WEYRWOMAN, SHE LEADS THE QUEENS' WINGS.

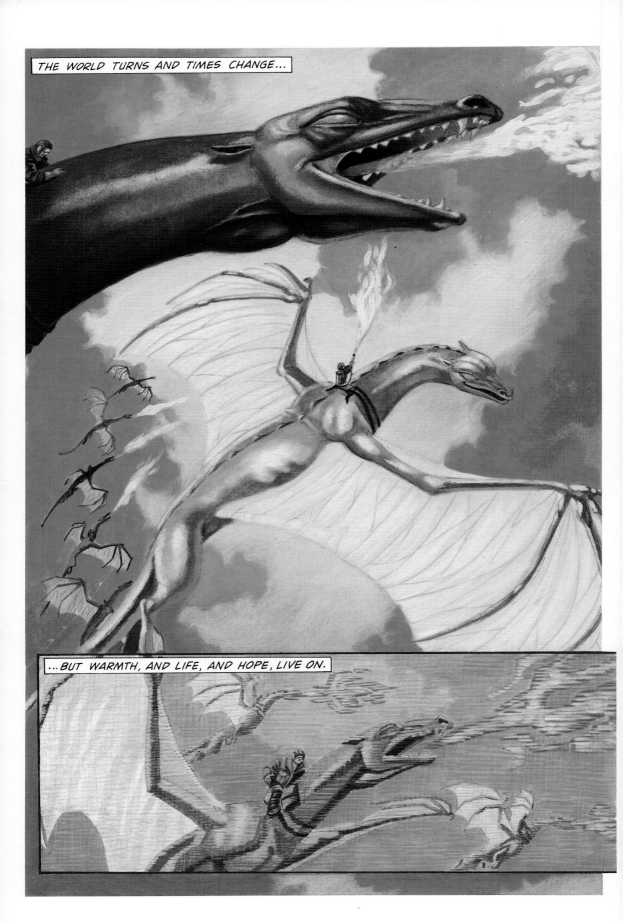

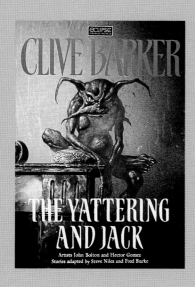

CLIVE BARKER'S
THE YATTERING AND JACK

Adapted by Steve Niles
Illustrated by John Bolton

A DARKLY HILARIOUS and weirdly perceptive tale of the devil at work from the acclaimed fantasist and master of horror fiction, Clive Barker.

Beelzebub sends his underling the Yattering to claim the soul of Jack Polo, pickle salesman. But in the Polo residence where the Yattering is bound, nothing doing. Polo's response, even to disaster, is merely to sigh, '*Que sera sera*'. The Yattering is going crazy. He must goad Polo to lunacy, the Old One insists. Polo was promised by his mother to the Lord of the Flies. And what match is a chronically dull pickle salesman for hell's own spawn . . . ? Find out.

Included in the same volume, a graphic adaptation of Clive Barker's short story *How Spoilers Bleed*, adapted by Steve Niles and Fred Burke, and illustrated by Hector Gomez. It tells of the gory revenge visited on white destroyers of the Brazilian jungle by the dying indigenous people of the Amazon basin. It is a punishment that fits the crime, incredibly unpleasant . . .

Clive Barker's bestselling works of fiction include *The Books of Blood, The Damnation Game, Weaveworld, Cabal, The Great and Secret Show, The Hellbound Heart , Imajica* and *The Thief of Always*. Not only is he prodigiously talented as a writer, he also produces and directs memorable films such as the *Hellraiser* trilogy, *Nightbreed* and *Candyman*, and is himself a spectacular visual artist. The illustrators he chooses to work with, therefore, John Bolton and Hector Gomez, are equally brilliant.

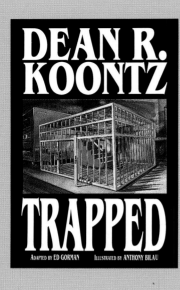

DEAN R. KOONTZ

TRAPPED

Adapted by Edward Gorman
Illustrated by Anthony Bilau

THE FIRST EVER graphic adaptation of a story
by the master of chilling fiction and chronicler of
midnight's menace, Dean R. Koontz.

Laboratory rats locked in a cage together - originally
they were kept in individual cages, but their aggressive
behaviour was so disturbing that they were put together
in the hope of quieting them. Instead it gives them the
chance they've been waiting for. They break out on a
stormy winter night. These are smart rats,
bioengineered and hostile, for some reason, to
humans. Perhaps because they were trapped . . .

But no longer. They take over the nearby house of
Meg Lassiter, two years a widow and mother to
Tommy, aged ten and with his leg in plaster from a
skiing fall. Meg and Tommy are trapped, now . . .
the rats' first victims.

Dean R. Koontz's inimitable style permeates the graphic
form, spreading evil and terror - and confronting them
with the force of a mother's need to protect her child.

Adapted by Edward Gorman and illustrated by
Anthony Bilau, this story of fear unleashed is realistic,
unnerving and moving.

NEIL GAIMAN

MIRACLEMAN:
THE GOLDEN AGE

Illustrated by Mark Buckingham

NEIL GAIMAN'S spectacular, mysterious, luminously strange and compelling saga of the all-British superhero and deity, Miracleman. *The Golden Age* is the age of miracles unimagined. It is the age of gods among men. It is the age of truth in which everything is what it seems, and nothing is as it was imagined.

'A work that transforms the superhero genre into something strange, wonderful, and politic. Excellent stuff!'

ALAN MOORE

MIRACLEMAN was given new life by Alan Moore, known as the King of the graphic novel, in the early 1980s. His and Gaiman's work is assessed in the critique below by Samuel R. Delany, author of *Dhalgren*, the *Nevèrÿon* series, and other science fiction masterpieces.

'Moore and Gaiman are the two writers who have done more to change the idea of what comics are and can be than anyone since . . . well, certainly since I started reading them in the 1940s. Reading Moore, followed by Gaiman, I found myself for the first time deeply, consistently, intensely interested in these comic book writers *as writers*. With that interest came a revision in the idea of what comics could be; they could be *written*, not just in a craftsman-like manner adequate to the visuals. The writing could be brilliant in itself. Here were writers with the range of language from silence to song - the whole of language with which to put across their stories. And the stories themselves! Gaiman's six entwined tales in *The Golden Age* come like sapphires afloat on a super-cooled liquid. They unfold like haiku. The voices they speak with are real. Their lambent characters, yearning both for bits of yesterday and portents of tomorrow, will linger with you long.'

SAMUEL R. DELANY

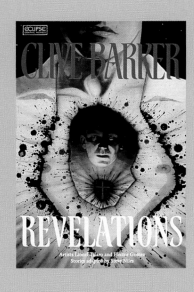

CLIVE BARKER'S
REVELATIONS

Adapted by Steve Niles
Illustrated by Lionel Talaro

ANOTHER CLIVE BARKER story of living mayhem and dying faith adapted for the graphic form by Steve Niles and illustrated by Lionel Talaro.

A murder thirty years ago, to the night, haunts the motel room where it happened - and where evangelist John Gyer and his unhappy wife Virginia are staying. Virginia senses the ghosts of Buck and Sadie Durning are near. But her dependence on pills to alleviate the oppressive effect her husband's "goodness" has on her lead her only to hideous dreams of violence. Observing her, the ghost Sadie, who was executed for the murder of her husband, is moved to sympathy. She is unrepentant, even though tonight she and the ghost of her husband have returned to the Cottonwood Motel to attempt a reconciliation beyond the grave. Virginia's problem is more compelling to her than Buck's lustful ghost. Before the clouds part to reveal a full moon, the blood-letting, the inevitable tragedy, will come to pass, again.

Clive Barker, the supreme fantasist, mixes life and death in a heady cocktail. Included in the same volume, an adaptation of his sinister story, *Babel's Children*, illustrated by Hector Gomez and adapted by Steve Niles.

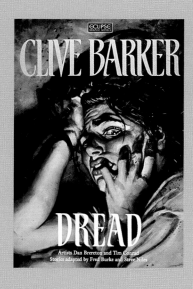

CLIVE BARKER'S
DREAD

Adapted by Fred Burke
Illustrated by Dan Brereton

WHAT DO YOU REALLY DREAD? Quaid, a student of philosophy, is interested to know. *Very* interested - as a hungry wolf is interested in red meat. Forget philosophy. Dread is at the heart of life. For Quaid, there is no delight the equal of dread, as long as it's someone else's. Cheryl Fromm's, for instance. Cheryl is bright, beautiful, dread-free, so she thinks. Even so, Quaid will teach her the meaning of fear . . . deliver her into dread. Quaid's friend Stephen Grace is sworn to silence on the Cheryl affair, but that won't save him, or Cheryl; and Quaid, of course, is both damned and doomed . . . to live the long night of his own dread. It is right to fear the darkness behind the door. No one escapes it. Open the door . . . to dread.

Adapted by Fred Burke and superbly, hauntingly illustrated by Dan Brereton, this is a graphic novel to linger over in appalled admiration at the extent of Clive Barker's understanding of his subject.

Also included in this volume, a graphic adaptation of Clive Barker's story, *Down Satan*. Adapted by Steve Niles and boldly illustrated by Tim Conrad, it tells of an atrocity waiting to happen: the New Hell built by one of the world's richest men to tempt the devil himself.